Sizzling Science

Lynn Huggins-Cooper

In a cave far away, lives a powerful wizard named Whimstaff. He spends his days finding the answers to ancient Science problems and has parchments filled with wonderful words. In this book, Whimstaff shares his knowledge to help you to master the art of Science.

Whimstaff has a goblin assistant named Pointy, who is very clever. Pointy helps Whimstaff perfect his spells and gets annoyed with the laziness of Mugly and Bugly, his fat pet frogs. They spend most of their time eating and sleeping and do as little work as possible.

Pointy also helps Whimstaff look after Miss Snufflebeam, a young dragon who is rather clumsy and often loses Whimstaff's words!

Wizard Whimstaff and his friends are very happy solving Science problems. Join them on a magical quest to win the Trophy of Science Wizardry!

Contents

Letts

Magical Muscles

My name is Miss Snufflebeam
and I live in the cave with Wizard Whimstaff.
I like to do exercise and Pointy told me that it is
my muscles and bones working together that help
me to move.

If I did not have bones, I would be all floppy!
Bones help us to stand up and move, and protect
soft parts of our bodies like our brains. Muscles
help our bones to move. When I bend my arm, the
muscles tighten up and help to pull the bones
where I want them to go.

Task 1 Do you know what your bones are called? Help me match the words below to the correct bones.

skull   ribs   backbone   pelvis   kneecap

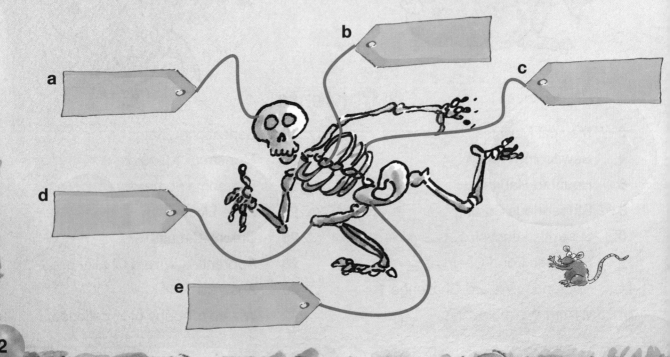

Task 2

My head hurts! Finish off these sentences to help me understand about bones and muscles. Fill the bones with the words in the box.

| ribs | tighten | muscles | floppy | bodies | skull |

a My brain is protected by my ⎨＿＿＿＿＿⎬ .

b My ⎨＿＿＿＿＿⎬ protect my heart and lungs and lots of other important body parts.

c Without bones, we would be ⎨＿＿＿＿＿⎬ and unable to stand up.

d When I bend my arm, the muscles ⎨＿＿＿＿＿⎬ up.

e ⎨＿＿＿＿＿⎬ help our bones to move.

f Bones support our ⎨＿＿＿＿＿⎬ and help us to stand up.

Task 3

You're clever! Now check these sentences. Are they true or false? Write **T** for true and **F** for false.

a The name of the bone that protects the brain is the spine.

b Our ribs are the bones that protect our heart and lungs.

c Bones support my body. Without them, I would be all floppy!

d Bones and muscles move together to help me move.

Sorcerer's Skill Check

Can you help me do this final exercise? Check that you know the names of all the bones we have talked about by writing them on the labels.

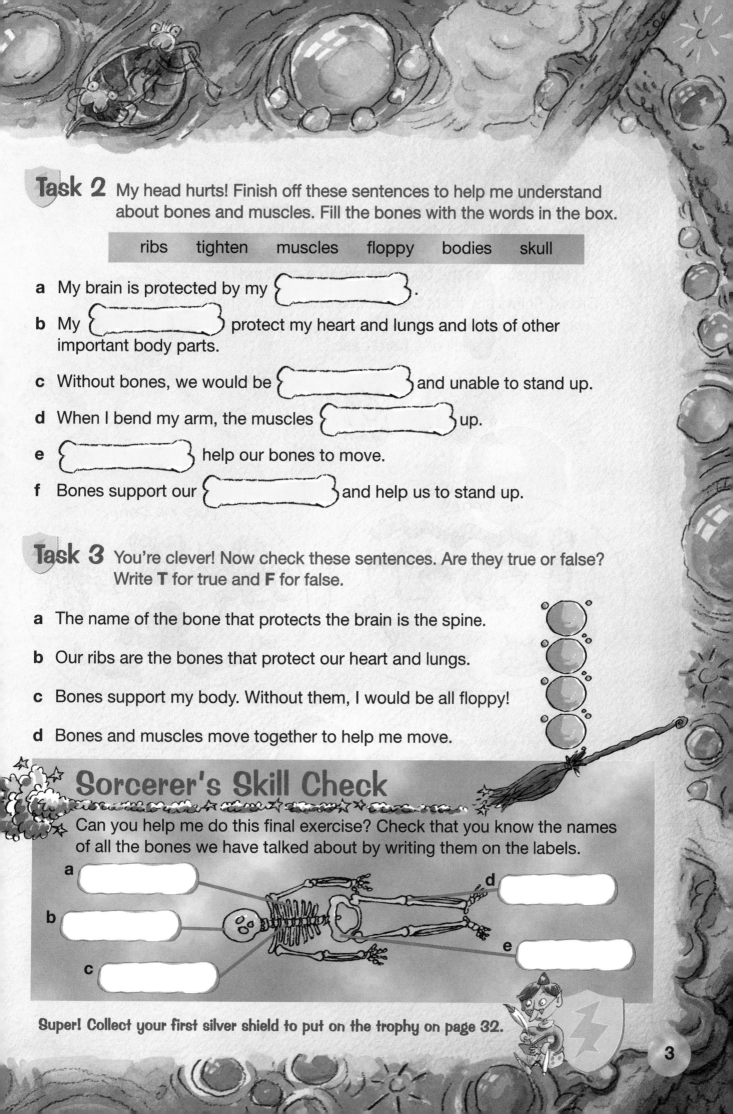

a ＿＿＿＿＿

b ＿＿＿＿＿

c ＿＿＿＿＿

d ＿＿＿＿＿

e ＿＿＿＿＿

Super! Collect your first silver shield to put on the trophy on page 32.

Bewitching Bones

We're Mugly and Bugly, Pointy's pet frogs. Everything Miss Snufflebeam said about bones is true! We have bones, too. But lots of other creatures don't, such as the bugs we like to eat! Slurp!

Croak! Animals without backbones often have other ways of supporting their bodies. They may have a shell or a hard case.

shell

hard case

Has bones

Has no bones

Task 1 Right, cleverclogs! Which animals in the list below have backbones? Draw them in this circle.

| tiger | jellyfish | lizard | worm | squid | ladybird | parrot |

Task 2

Very clever! But can you work out which animals in this picture do not have backbones? We think lots of them are delicious! Burp! Draw a circle around the animals without backbones.

Task 3

Look at these animals. Which ones have a shell or hardcase instead of bones? Draw a circle around the ones you choose.

a   b   c   d   e

f   g   h   i   j

Sorcerer's Skill Check

Finally, check that you have remembered which animals have backbones and which do not, while we have a snooze! Draw a circle around the animals with backbones.

a   b   c   d   e   f

Magic yourself another silver shield for your trophy, young apprentice!

Haunted Habitats

I'm Wizard Whimstaff and I'm going to help you become a science wizard! I have been building some special places for my pets to live. A pond for Mugly and Bugly, and special nooks and crannies in the cave for my bats. The place where animals and plants live is called their habitat.

A pond is a habitat. The desert and the seashore are also habitats.

Task 1 Match the creatures and plants to their habitat. Some live in a wood and others live on the seashore. Write **W** in the box for the animals and plants from the woods, and **S** in the box for the animals that live on the seashore.

a seaweed   b tree   c crab   d fish   e owl   f squirrel

Task 2 Excellent, young apprentice! Now try this. Draw the animals and plants from the desert on the desert picture and the animals and plants that live in or near a pond on the pond scene.

frog   newt   scorpion   camel   tadpole   dragonfly   rattlesnake   heron   cactus

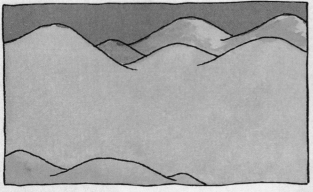

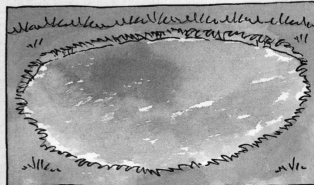

Task 3 Well done! Now try this last pair of habitats! Draw a leaf shape around the animals and plants that live in the rainforest, and a star shape around the animals and plants that live in the snowy polar regions.

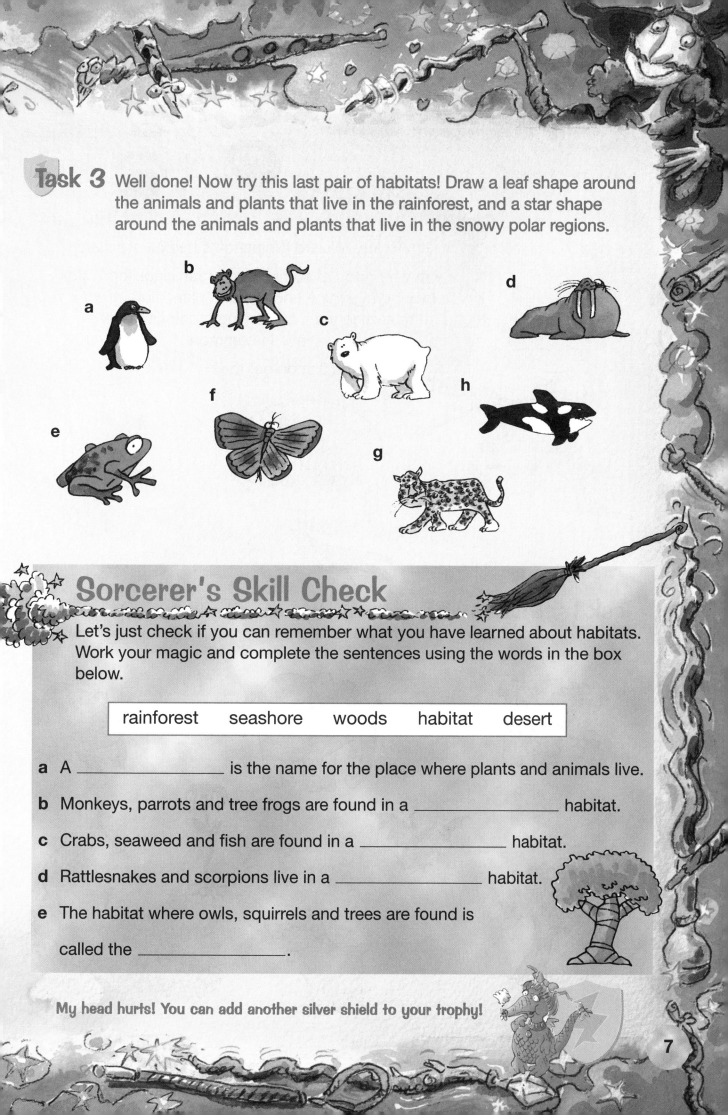

Sorcerer's Skill Check

Let's just check if you can remember what you have learned about habitats. Work your magic and complete the sentences using the words in the box below.

| rainforest | seashore | woods | habitat | desert |

a A _____ is the name for the place where plants and animals live.

b Monkeys, parrots and tree frogs are found in a _____ habitat.

c Crabs, seaweed and fish are found in a _____ habitat.

d Rattlesnakes and scorpions live in a _____ habitat.

e The habitat where owls, squirrels and trees are found is

called the _____.

My head hurts! You can add another silver shield to your trophy!

7

Stupendous Sorting

I'm Pointy, Wizard Whimstaff's helpful assistant!

I'm very good at sorting and organising! Today I'm looking at sorting animals and plants into groups. I'm sorting them by looking at things that they have in common.

You'll soon get the hang of it!

has fur   has no fur

Task 1 Sort these into two groups of plants and animals. Draw a line from the plant shape to all of the plants and a line from the bat shape to all the animals. Super!

Task 2 Well done! Now, see if you can sort these animals into two groups of has a shell and has no shell. Draw a circle around the animals with shells.

a   b   c   d   e   f

Task 3 You have done very well, but practice makes perfect! Sort these animals into two groups of can fly and cannot fly. Write **F** in the hats under the animals that can fly.

a   b   c   d   e   f

Sorcerer's Skill Check

Nearly there! Look at these animals. Sort them into two groups of lays eggs and does not lay eggs. Draw an egg shape around the animals that lay eggs.

a   b   c   d   e   f

Croak! Time to grab another silver shield for your trophy, while we have a snack!

Lustrous Lifecycles

All living things change as they grow. A cat starts out as a tiny kitten, then keeps getting bigger until it is an adult.

But a frog changes completely. Mugly and Bugly started out as frogspawn, then changed into tadpoles and finally grew into frogs!

Task 1 Can you help me to put this hen lifecycle in order? Like a dragon's lifecycle, it starts with an egg! Write the numbers in the correct order.

a b c d

Task 2 You are clever! I'm having a very muddled day. Can you put this frog lifecycle in order? Write the numbers in the correct order, starting with the youngest.

a b c d

Task 3 Abracadada! Now draw a butterfly lifecycle. Draw pictures in the boxes to put the lifecycle in the correct order.

a → b → c → d

Task 4 Oh dear, I'm still confused! Can you put this plant lifecycle in order for me? Draw the lifecycle in the boxes.

sunflower · seed · seedling

a → b → c

Sorcerer's Skill Check

Finally, test your magical skills and put this human lifecycle in order, from the youngest to the oldest.

a   b   c   d   e

Super! Stick a silver shield on your trophy!

Fantastic Food Chains

All creatures have to eat. Miss Snufflebeam likes fruit, and Mugly and Bugly like bugs!

Even plants need energy. They make their food using sunlight. Animals eat the plants and then those animals are eaten by other animals. The energy passes from plant to animal, and on to other animals. This is called a food chain.

You'll soon get the hang of it!

eaten by

eaten by

eaten by

Task 1

Now, put this woodland food chain in the correct order. Write the numbers in the boxes.

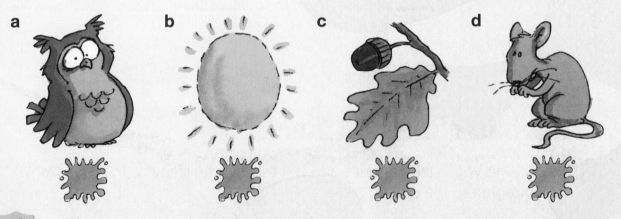

a   b   c   d

Task 2

Super! Now try this seashore food chain. Write the words in the boxes to put the food chain in the right order.

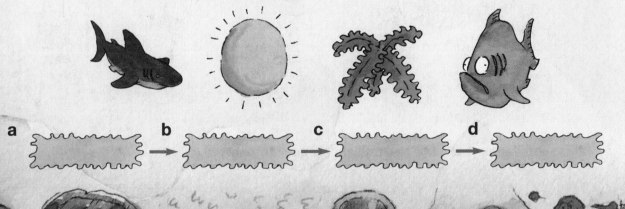

a → b → c → d

Task 3 Great work! Can you put this garden food chain in order? Draw the food chain in the correct order here in the garden.

| snail | blackbird | Sun | cat | lettuce |

a ⇒ b ⇒ c ⇒ d ⇒ e

Task 4 Well done! Now put this food chain in order. Write the numbers in the boxes.

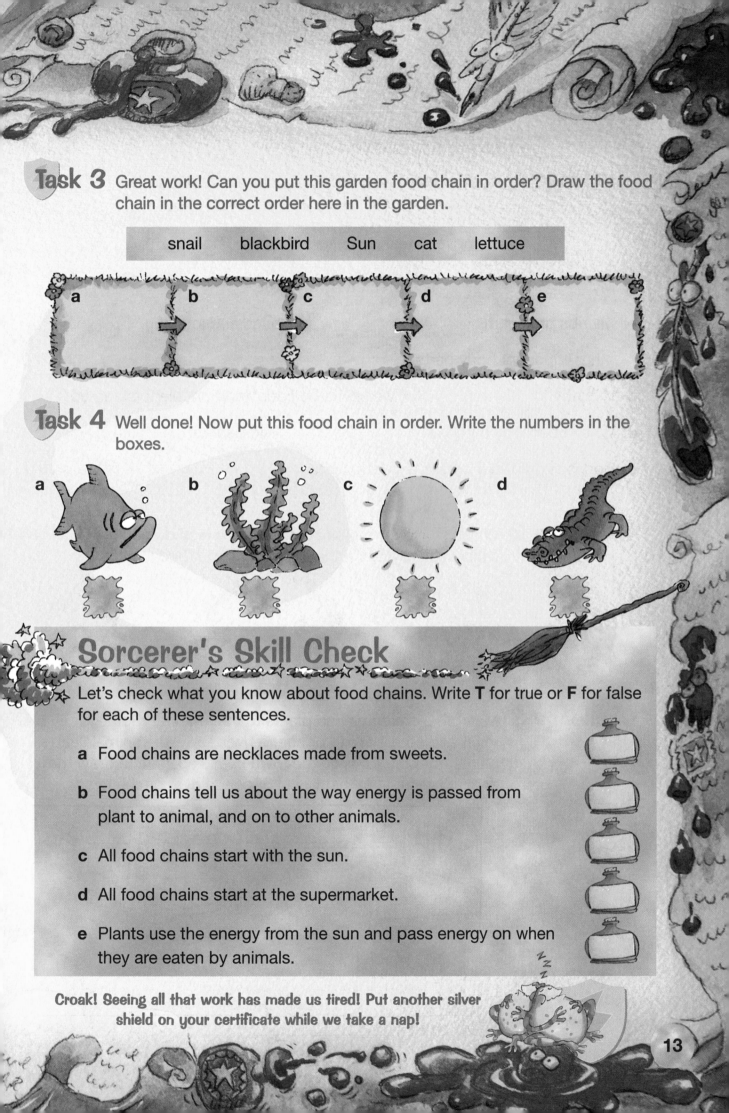

a   b   c   d

Sorcerer's Skill Check

Let's check what you know about food chains. Write **T** for true or **F** for false for each of these sentences.

a Food chains are necklaces made from sweets.

b Food chains tell us about the way energy is passed from plant to animal, and on to other animals.

c All food chains start with the sun.

d All food chains start at the supermarket.

e Plants use the energy from the sun and pass energy on when they are eaten by animals.

Croak! Seeing all that work has made us tired! Put another silver shield on your certificate while we take a nap!

Apprentice Wizard Challenge 1

Challenge 1 Answer these questions about bones and muscles. Fill the gaps with the words in the box.

> move   heart   muscles   brain   bones

a My _____ is protected by my skull.

b My ribs protect my _____ and lungs and lots of other important body parts.

c Without _____, we would be floppy and unable to stand up.

d When I bend my arm, the _____ tighten up.

e Bones support our bodies and help us to _____.

Challenge 2 Which animals have backbones and which do not? Draw a wiggly shape around the animals without backbones!

a    **b**    **c**   **d**   **e**

Challenge 3 Match the creatures and plants to their habitat. Some live in the town and others live in or near a river. Draw the animals and plants from the town on the town in this scene and draw the animals and plants that live in or near a river on the river.

Challenge 4 Sort these animals into two groups, those that have feathers and those that don't have feathers. Draw a circle around the animals with feathers.

Challenge 5 Put this duck lifecycle in order. Write the numbers in the correct order, from the youngest to the oldest.

a

b

c

d

Challenge 6 Put this forest food chain in the correct order. Draw the food chain in the box below.

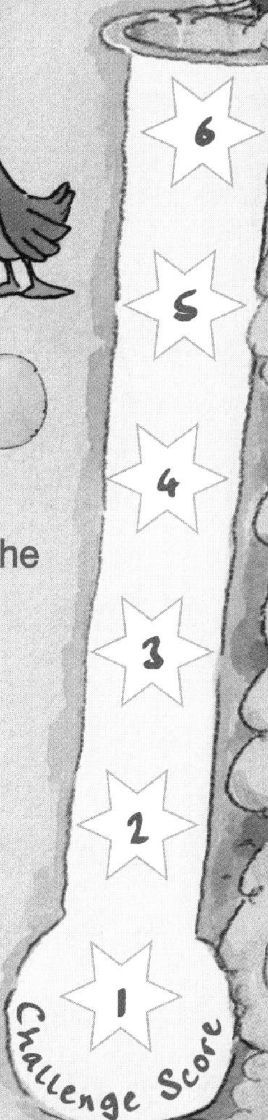

→

→

Count how many challenges you got right and put stars on the test tube to show your score. Then have a silver shield for your trophy!

6

5

4

3

2

1

Challenge Score

15

Wizard Warmers

It's time to learn about keeping warm! The cave can get very cold, so I'm an expert! Some materials keep things warm. Think about the woolly socks, fleece coats and thick duvets we use in winter! Many work by trapping air, which our bodies warm up.

Some materials heat up quickly. Metal heats up quickly, which is why my cooking pans are made of metal. The handles are made of wood, though. It doesn't heat up quickly, so I can hold the handles without burning my hands.

Task 1 Which clothes in the picture below would you wear in cold weather? Draw a circle around the clothes you would choose. Allakazan!

a   b 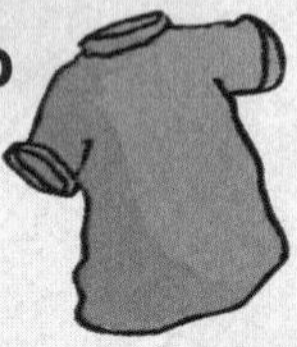   c 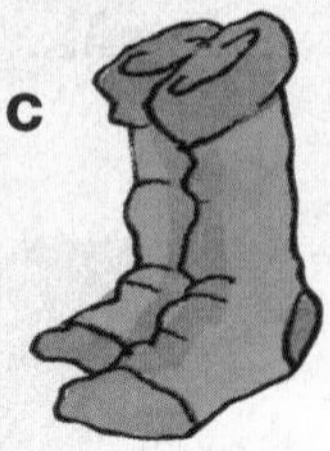   d 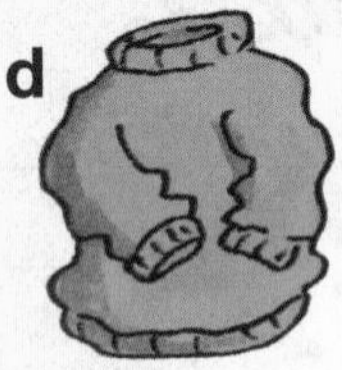   e    f

Task 2 Well done, young apprentice! Now finish off these sentences. Use the words in the box to fill the gaps.

metal   air   heat   cool   coat

a In cold weather, I wear a fleecy _____ to keep me warm.

b Pans are made from _____, because it heats up quickly.

c Some fabrics trap _____. This heats up and keeps us warm.

d Pan handles are made of wood, because it does not _____ up quickly.

e In summer, we wear thin clothes to keep us _____.

Design an outfit to keep a wizard like me warm in winter. Write a few labels to show how the clothes would keep me warm. Hey presto!

Sorcerer's Skill Check

Well done, young apprentice! Now look at the pictures below. I'm sorting out Miss Snufflebeam's clothing, as it's all in a muddle! I want to put her summer clothes away and keep her winter clothes out ready for her to wear. Draw the clothes I should put away in this suitcase shape.

a   b   c

d   e   f

g   h   i   j

Dabracababra! Now I'll keep warm! Stick another silver shield on your trophy.

Sensational States

I'm organising things again! Some of these bottles of potion are nearly empty. One thing I've found is that it doesn't matter what shape bottle I pour the liquid into, it still takes up the same space.

I'm also having fun heating potions to turn them into gases, then I can keep them in these magic balloons. They take up less shelf space when they're floating in the air!

Practice makes perfect!

Task 1 See if you're as easy to fool as Miss Snufflebeam! Look at the potion bottle and put a tick (✔) in the box to show which container holds the most. Supe

a

100ml

80ml

☐ ☐

b

70ml

90ml

☐ ☐

c

120ml

150ml

☐ ☐

Task 2 This bottle contains 100ml of newt juice. If I pour it into this short fat jug, how much will there be in the jug?

100ml

_____ml

Task 3 I need to put these ingredients in the correct place. Some are liquids and others are gases. Write **G** for gas and **L** for liquid in the jars. It's easy when you know how!

a air　　**b** water　　**c** oxygen　　**d** steam　　**e** frog juice　**f** cola

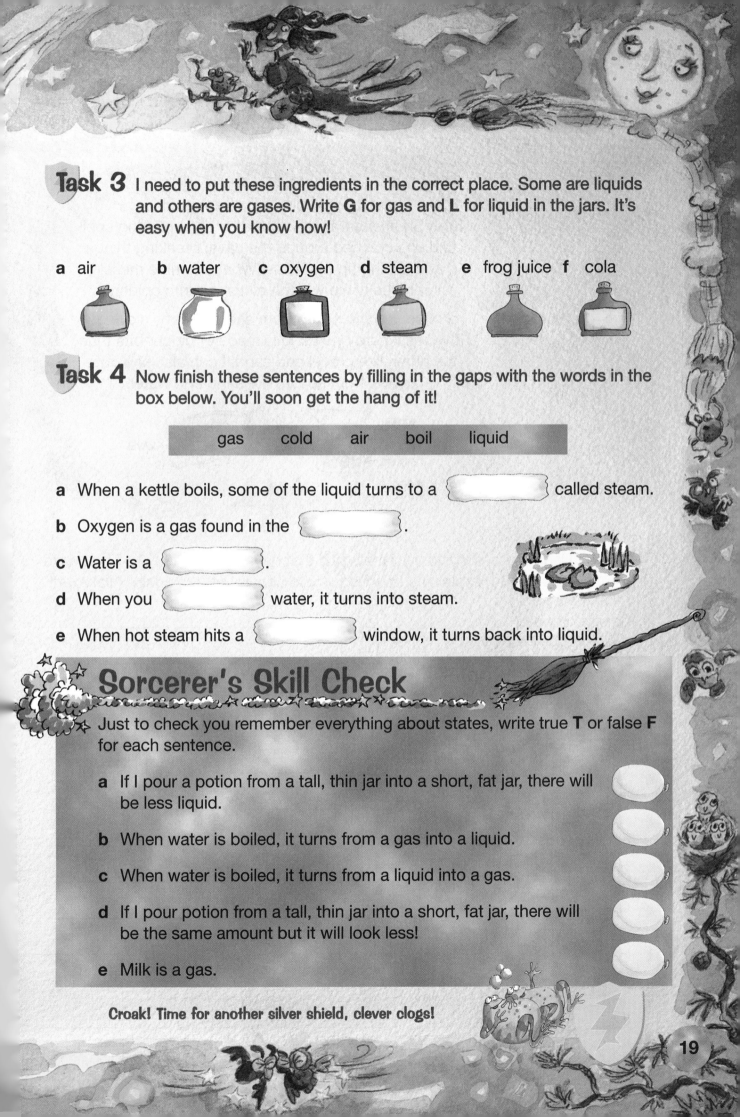

Task 4 Now finish these sentences by filling in the gaps with the words in the box below. You'll soon get the hang of it!

gas　　cold　　air　　boil　　liquid

a When a kettle boils, some of the liquid turns to a _____ called steam.

b Oxygen is a gas found in the _____ .

c Water is a _____ .

d When you _____ water, it turns into steam.

e When hot steam hits a _____ window, it turns back into liquid.

Sorcerer's Skill Check

Just to check you remember everything about states, write true **T** or false **F** for each sentence.

a If I pour a potion from a tall, thin jar into a short, fat jar, there will be less liquid.

b When water is boiled, it turns from a gas into a liquid.

c When water is boiled, it turns from a liquid into a gas.

d If I pour potion from a tall, thin jar into a short, fat jar, there will be the same amount but it will look less!

e Milk is a gas.

Croak! Time for another silver shield, clever clogs!

Monstrous Mixtures

I need your help, young apprentice. Miss Snufflebeam was scared by an exploding spell and she crashed around the cave, breaking things and mixing up materials! What a terrible mess! We're lucky we weren't all turned into spiders!

I'm separating solids from each other by sieving. It works where one thing is made of bigger bits than the other, like gravel and sand. I can also separate liquids from solids, like sand and water.

WATER
GRAVEL
SIEVE
GRAVEL
SAND

Task 1 Read the descriptions of materials that have been mixed up. Then write a sentence, explaining how you would separate them again. Allakazan!

a Sand and water

_____

_____

_____

b Sand and gravel

_____

_____

_____

c Fine sawdust and stones

_____

_____

_____

d Cornflakes and sugar

_____

_____

_____

Task 2 Miss Snufflebeam is making chocolate chip cookies! Can you number these instructions in the correct order to show her how to separate the chocolate chips from the flour?

a Put the mixture of chocolate chips and flour in the sieve.

b The flour will collect in the dish, but the chocolate chips are too big to go through the holes in the sieve.

c Collect the things you need – a sieve and two dishes.

d Shake the sieve gently over the dish.

Task 3 This is hard, but do your best! Write instructions to explain to Miss Snufflebeam how to separate sand from water. Use the words in the box to help you.

sand	water	sieve	jug	beaker	pour

Sorcerer's Skill Check

Wonderful work! Just check that you have remembered everything by completing these sentences. Use the words in the box to fill the gaps.

liquid	mixture	separated

a Water and sand can be _____ by pouring the mixture through a strainer.

b Water and sand can be separated because water is a _____ that pours through the strainer, but sand is a solid and is caught in the strainer.

c Gravel and sand can be separated by shaking the _____ gently through a sieve.

Practice made you perfect! Pop another silver shield on your trophy!

Fearsome Forces

Croak! When we swim, we push our way through the water with our strong legs. The water pushes back on us, though. When we try to swim to the bottom, the force that pushes back up against us is called upthrust. Sometimes we bob back to the surface like corks!

When Wizard Whimstaff flies on his broomstick, he gets slowed down by air resistance and friction. That is a force that pushes against things like cars and trains as they move.

When it is icy, Miss Snufflebeam slips so we put down sand. That makes friction, which stops her from slipping. She rubs her cold hands together to warm them and that is friction, too!

Task 1 Brain cell alert! **Friction**, **air resistance** or **upthrust**? Write the correct word in the boxes. Be careful, it's harder than it looks!

a A frog diving feels [   ].

b An aeroplane feels friction and [   ] as it flies.

c [   ] stops us from slipping over.

d Ships float because of [   ].

Task 2 Slurp! Look at the pictures below. Write the correct force under the picture.

a

b

c

d

_____ _____ _____ _____

_____ _____ _____ _____

Task 3 Test yourself with these, while we have a snooze.

a Draw a picture of us – Mugly and Bugly – swimming. Add a label to show the force that acts on us when we swim!

b Draw a picture of Wizard Whimstaff flying his broomstick. Add a label to show the force that acts on him as he flies.

Sorcerer's Skill Check

Grub's up! But before we go, write **T** for true or **F** for false.

a Upthrust pushes swimmers to the bottom of the pool.

b Upthrust pushes up against the bottom of boats and makes them float.

c Friction between the soles of our shoes and the pavement is what makes us slip over.

d Friction between the soles of our shoes and the pavement is what stops us from slipping over.

e Air resistance makes aeroplanes – and wizards – fly faster!

f Air resistance makes aeroplanes – and wizards – slow down as they fly.

Add another silver shield to your trophy. Super!

Eerie Electricity

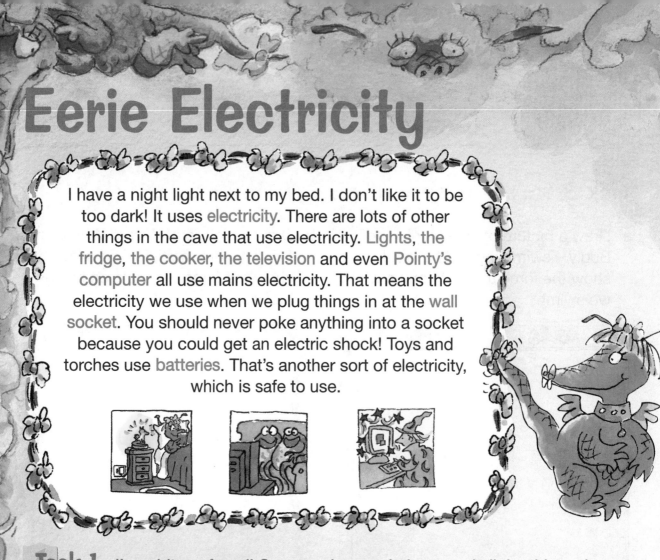

I have a night light next to my bed. I don't like it to be too dark! It uses electricity. There are lots of other things in the cave that use electricity. Lights, the fridge, the cooker, the television and even Pointy's computer all use mains electricity. That means the electricity we use when we plug things in at the wall socket. You should never poke anything into a socket because you could get an electric shock! Toys and torches use batteries. That's another sort of electricity, which is safe to use.

Task 1 I'm a bit confused! Can you draw a circle around all the things that use electricity?

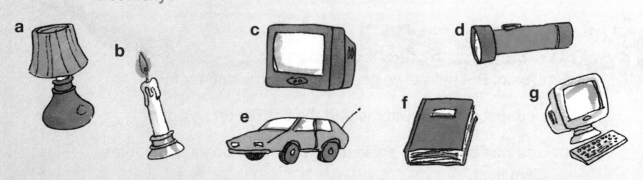

Task 2 My head hurts! Can you help me to learn the difference between mains and battery electricity? Draw a circle around all the things that use mains electricity. I've done the first one for you.

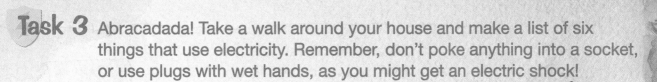

Task 3 Abracadada! Take a walk around your house and make a list of six things that use electricity. Remember, don't poke anything into a socket, or use plugs with wet hands, as you might get an electric shock!

a _____   d _____

_____   _____

b _____   e _____

_____   _____

c _____   f _____

_____   _____

Sorcerer's Skill Check

Just to check you have understood all about electricity, how many things can you see in the cave that use electricity? Draw a circle around them for me.

Brain cell alert! Time to add another sticker to your trophy.

Creepy Circuits

Wizard Whimstaff lets me use his equipment to do experiments! Today I'm using batteries, bulbs and wires to make circuits.

The circuit has to be complete for a bulb to light. If the wires are not joined correctly to the battery and bulb, the bulb will not light. It's quite complicated!

Never open a battery! They contain chemicals that can harm you!

Task 1 Look at these circuits. Put a cross (✗) by the ones that will not light the bulb. It's easy when you know how!

a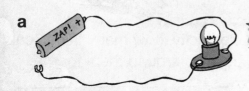

d

b

e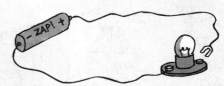

c

Task 2 Super! Complete the sentences using the words in the box to fill the gaps.

| bulb | circuits | wires | batteries | light |

a For a bulb to light, the _____ need to be connected to the battery and bulb correctly.

b If the _____ are the wrong way round in a circuit, the bulb will not light.

c If the wires in a circuit are not joined correctly to the battery and bulb, the _____ will not light.

d Batteries, bulbs and wires are all used to build _____ .

e A circuit has to be complete for a bulb to _____ .

Task 3 Now, mark these sentences **T** for true or **F** for false. Practice makes perfect!

a A bulb will still light, even if the wires are not connected properly.

b All the wires need to be connected properly for a bulb to light.

c You should never try to open or cut a battery – it is dangerous!

d It does not matter if the batteries are the wrong way round in a circuit.

Sorcerer's Skill Check

To check you have remembered what it takes to make a bulb light, use your magic and draw a circuit that will work in the space below.

Fine work, young apprentice! Add another silver shield to your trophy.

Apprentice Wizard Challenge 2

Challenge 1
Design an outfit to keep Pointy warm in winter. Write some labels to show how the clothes would keep him warm.

Challenge 2
Write down the highest amount of each pair of bottles.

a

180ml 190ml

b

90ml 70ml

c

140ml 120ml

Challenge 3
Can you put these instructions in the correct order by numbering the ink splats from 1 to 5 to show how to separate pebbles from compost?

a Put the mixture of compost and pebbles in the sieve.

b Collect the things you need – a sieve and two containers.

c Pour the pebbles into the second dish.

d The compost will collect in the container, but the pebbles are too big to go through the holes in the sieve.

e Shake the sieve gently over a container.

Challenge 4 Name that force! Friction, air resistance or upthrust? Write the correct word in the boxes.

a A person diving feels [＿＿＿＿＿＿] .

b A wizard feels friction and [＿＿＿＿＿＿＿＿＿＿] as he flies on his broomstick.

c [＿＿＿＿＿＿] stops us from slipping on icy days, so we wear boots with rough soles to grip.

d On a rough surface, we do not slip because our shoes make lots of [＿＿＿＿＿＿] .

e When I float my rubber duck in the bath, it floats because of [＿＿＿＿＿＿] .

Challenge 5 Join the things that use battery electricity to the battery with a line.

a   b   c   d   e   f

Challenge 6 Look at these circuits. Draw a circle around the one that will light the bulb.

a   – ZAP! +

b   – ZAP! +

c   – ZAP! +

6
5
4
3
2
1
Challenge Score

Count how many challenges you got right and put stars on the test tube to show your score. Then take the last silver shield for your trophy!

Answers

Pages 2–3

Task 1
- **a** skull
- **b** backbone
- **c** ribs
- **d** kneecap
- **e** pelvis

Task 2
- **a** skull
- **b** ribs
- **c** floppy
- **d** tighten
- **e** muscles
- **f** bodies

Task 3
- **a** F   **b** T
- **c** T   **d** T

Sorcerer's Skill Check
- **a** ribs
- **b** skull
- **c** backbone
- **d** kneecap
- **e** pelvis

Pages 4–5

Task 1 Drawings of these creatures: tiger, lizard and parrot.

Task 2

Task 3

The tortoise isn't circled as it has bones as well as a shell.

Sorcerer's Skill Check

Pages 6–7

Task 1
- **a** S   **b** W   **c** S
- **d** S   **e** W   **f** W

Task 2 Desert: scorpion, camel, rattlesnake and cactus.
Pond: frog, newt, tadpole, dragonfly and heron.

Task 3

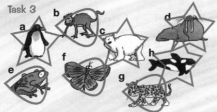

Sorcerer's Skill Check
- **a** habitat
- **b** rainforest
- **c** seashore
- **d** desert
- **e** woods

Pages 8–9

Task 1

Task 2

Task 3 a, c, e and f should have **F** written under them

Sorcerer's Skill Check

Pages 10–11

Task 1
- 1 **a**   2 **c**
- 3 **d**   4 **b**

Task 2
- 1 **c**   2 **a**
- 3 **d**   4 **b**

Task 3

Task 4

Sorcerer's Skill Check
- 1 **b**   2 **d**   3 **a**
- 4 **c**   5 **e**

Pages 12–13

Task 1
- 1 **b**   2 **c**
- 3 **d**   4 **a**

Task 2
- **a** sun
- **b** seaweed
- **c** fish
- **d** shark

Task 3

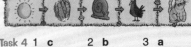

Task 4
- 1 **c**   2 **b**   3 **a**
- 4 **d**

Sorcerer's Skill Check
- **a** F   **b** T   **c** T
- **d** F   **e** T

Pages 14–15

Challenge 1
- **a** brain
- **b** heart
- **c** bones
- **d** muscles
- **e** move

Challenge 2

Challenge 3

The snail could be in either the town or the river scene.

Challenge 4

Challenge 5
- 1 **b**   2 **c**
- 3 **d**   4 **a**

Challenge 6

Pages 16–17

Task 1

Task 2 a coat
  b metal
  c air
  d heat
  e cool

Task 3 The picture should include warm materials, that cover his entire body, to keep the wizard warm.

Sorcerer's Skill Check

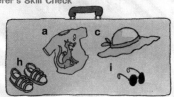

Pages 18–19

Task 1 a 100ml **b** 90ml **c** 150ml

Task 2 100ml

Task 3 a G **b** L **c** G
  d G **e** L **f** L

Task 4 a gas
  b air
  c liquid
  d boil
  e cold

Sorcerer's Skill Check
  a F **b** F **c** T
  d T **e** F

Pages 20–21

Task 1 a A sentence that suggests filtering materials.
  b A sentence that suggests sieving materials.
  c A sentence that suggests sieving materials.
  d A sentence that suggests sieving materials.

Task 2 1 c **2 a**
  3 d **4 b**

Task 3 Pour mixture through the sieve into the beaker. The water will run through the sieve into the jug and the sand will be left in the sieve. Remove the sand and place it in the beaker.

Sorcerer's Skill Check
  a separated
  b liquid
  c mixture

Pages 22–23

Task 1 a upthrust
  b air resistance
  c friction
  d upthrust

Task 2 a upthrust
  b friction
  c air resistance
  d friction

Task 3 a

upthrust   upthrust

b

air resistance

Sorcerer's Skill Check
  a F **b** T **c** F
  d T **e** F **f** T

Pages 24–25

Task 1

Task 2

Task 3 Answers will vary, but could include TV, video, computer.

Sorcerer's Skill Check

Pages 26–27

Task 1 a, b, d, e will not light the bulb.

Task 2 a wires
  b batteries
  c bulb
  d circuits
  e light

Task 3 a F **b** T **c** T
  d F

Sorcerer's Skill Check
  An example drawing would be:

Pages 28–29

Challenge 1
  Picture of an outfit containing materials that keep Pointy warm, like fleece, hat etc.

Challenge 2
  a 190ml **b** 90ml **c** 140ml

Challenge 3
  1 b **2 a** **3 e**
  4 d **5 c**

Challenge 4
  a upthrust
  b air resistance
  c friction
  d friction
  e upthrust

Challenge 5

Challenge 6
  Circuit c lights the bulb.

The end

Wizard's Trophy of Excellence

Magical Muscles

Bewitching Bones

Wizard Warmers

Sensational States

 Haunted Habitats

Stupendous Sorting

 Monstrous Mixtures

 Fearsome Forces

Lustrous Lifecycles

Fantastic Food Chains

Eerie Electricity

Creepy Circuits

 Apprentice Wizard Challenge 1

 **Apprentice Wizard Challenge 2**

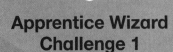

This is to state that Wizard Whimstaff awards

Apprentice _____

the Trophy of Science Wizardry. Congratulations!

Published 2003
10 9 8 7 6 5 4

Letts Educational, The Chiswick Centre,
414 Chiswick High Road, London W4 5TF
Tel 0845 602 1937   Fax 020 8742 8767
Email mail@lettsed.co.uk
www.Letts-SuccessZone.com

Text, design and illustrations © Letts Educational Ltd 2003

Author: Lynn Huggins-Cooper
Book Concept and Development:
Helen Jacobs, Publishing Director; Sophie London, Project Editor
Design and Editorial: 2idesign ltd, Cambridge
Cover Design: Linda Males
Illustrations: Mike Phillips (Beehive Illustration)
Cover Illustration: Neil Chapman (Beehive Illustration)

British Library Cataloguing in Publication Data

A CIP record for this book is available from the British Library.

ISBN 978-1-84315-132-6

Printed in Italy

Colour reproduction by PDQ Repro Limited, Bungay, Suffolk.